THE CORDELIA DREAM

MARINA CARR

The Royal Shakespeare Company

The Royal Shakespeare Company is one of the world's best known theatre ensembles, performing throughout the year in Stratford-upon-Avon, with regular residencies in London and Newcastle, and tours both in the UK and abroad.

Shakespeare is our in-house playwright, and central to the work of the RSC is the opportunity to investigate his influence on modern and contemporary writers. Further, our Shakespearean productions become shallow unless they relate to contemporary work which deals directly with the world we live in.

The RSC's commitment to modern classics and new work can clearly be seen in our repertoire. We will be producing more new plays over the coming seasons, and working with living writers in the Shakespeare rehearsal room. The writer's imagination will become part of the natural conversation as the ensemble investigate the plays.

We hope and believe that this reconnection of living writers with our house playwright will become one of the most mutually nourishing relationships in theatre. Shakespeare is a great teacher. His influence on contemporary writers cannot be underestimated. He knows how to marry the recognisable with the lyrical and entertainment with high art. He knows how to marry the epic with the intimate. There is a vast array of skills and stagecraft which we are inviting contemporary dramatists to plunder – just so long as they roll their sleeves up and join the actors, directors, musicians and designers in wrestling Shakespeare's beauty and vigour onto our stages.

Introduction

One of the great pleasures of working with new plays at the RSC is seeing just how many contemporary dramatists are seeking treatment for their addiction to Shakespeare. We seem to have a generation of playwrights who carry Shakespeare around with them in their handbags and briefcases. Where once all roads led to Chekhov and finely calibrated understatement we are now seeing a generation of writers who want to brave the six-lane motorway that leads to Shakespeare, the Greeks and epic playwriting. We are now witnessing playwrights embracing more flamboyant influences and possibilities.

Marina Carr was a bold playwright long before we commissioned her but with this play she is addressing themes that have long haunted her and to which Shakespeare gives voice. Drawing from the storehouse of Irish myth and inspired by Shakespeare's emotional fearlessness she has written a two-hander which is quite unlike her previous work.

Marina is at once an Irish voice and with an imagination that is without borders. She feels very at home on our stages. Her rich, muscular, poetic language fits effortlessly amongst our repertoire.

I hope you enjoy *The Cordelia Dream*.

Michael Boyd
RSC Artistic Director

The RSC Ensemble is generously supported by
THE GATSBY CHARITABLE FOUNDATION and THE KOVNER FOUNDATION

The RSC Literary Department is generously supported by
THE DRUE HEINZ TRUST

The RSC's New Work is generously supported by
CHRISTOPHER SETON ABELE on behalf of THE ARGOSY FOUNDATION

The RSC is grateful for the significant support of its principal funder,
Arts Council England, without which our work would not be possible.
Around 50 per cent of the RSC's income is self-generated from Box Office sales,
sponsorship, donations, enterprise and partnerships with other organisations.

The RSC was established in 1961, but its history stretches back to 1879
when the first permanent theatre was built in Stratford on the site of
the current Royal Shakespeare and Swan Theatres.

Production Acknowledgments

Scenery, set painting, properties, costumes, armoury, wigs and make-up
by RSC Workshops, Stratford-upon-Avon.
Deputy Head of Casting Lucy Jenkins CDG.
Production photographer Simon Annand.
Access performances provided by Mary Plackett, Ellie Packer and Julia Grundy.

This production of *The Cordelia Dream* was first performed
by the Royal Shakespeare Company at Wilton's Music Hall, London,
on 11 December 2008. The cast was as follows:

WOMAN	**Michelle Gomez**
MAN	**David Hargreaves**

Directed by	**Selina Cartmell**
Designed by	**Giles Cadle**
Lighting designed by	**Matthew Richardson**
Music by	**Conor Linehan**
Sound designed by	**Fergus O'Hare**
Movement by	**Anna Morrissey**
Company Dramaturg	**Jeanie O'Hare**
Company text and voice work by	**Stephen Kemble**
Music Director	**Eloise Prouse**
Casting by	**Sam Jones CDG**
Production Manager	**Pete Griffin**
Costume Supervisor	**Lisa Trump**
Company Manager	**Katie Vine**
Company Stage Manager	**Alix Harvey-Thompson**
Deputy Stage Manager	**Alison Daniels**
Assistant Stage Manager	**Sarah Caselton-Smith**

Musicians

Violin	**Eloise Prouse**
Viola	**Amy Wein**
Cello	**Ben Davies**
Piano recording	**Conor Linehan**

This text may differ slightly from the play as performed.

The Wilton's Music Hall season is generously supported by
THE WILLIAMS CHARITABLE TRUST

MICHELLE GOMEZ
Woman

RSC: *The Taming of the Shrew*.
trained: RSAMD.
theatre includes: *Boeing Boeing*, *Trainspotting* (West End); *The Vagina Monologues* (Arts Theatre/Royal Albert Hall); *Relative Values* (Richmond/No. 1 tour); *Abandonment* (Traverse); *The Pleasure Man*, *Cavalcade*, *The Double* (Citizens Theatre); *The Communist Manifesto* (Volcano Theatre Co. UK tour); *Sleep With Me* (National Theatre); *Of Blessed Memory* (King's Head); *Seizer* (Edinburgh Festival); *Headstate* (Greenwich Festival/Edinburgh Festival); *The Merchant of Venice* (Brunton); *The Android Circuit* (Winged Horse tour); *The Master Builder* (Royal Lyceum); *The Jewess of Toledo* (Bridewell); *Barabbas* (Tramway); *Play Boy* (Boilerhouse Theatre Co. Edinburgh Festival Award); *The Sneeze* (CCA); *Skinny Spew* (Chandler Studio); *Find Me* (New Athenaeum).
television includes: *Oliver Twist*, *Wedding Belles* (nominated Scottish BAFTA for Best Actress), *Feel the Force*, *Carrie and Barry*, *Green Wing*, *Murder in Suburbia*, *The Book Group* (nominated Scottish BAFTA for Best TV Performance), *Good Housekeeping Guide*, *Ready When You Are Mr McGill*, *Manchild*, *My Family*, *Rebus*, *The Raven*, *Taggart*, *Pinkerton Files*, *The Ladies' Man*, *Para Handy*, *First and Last*.
film includes: *Chromophobia*, *Subterrain* (short), *The Wrong Blonde*, *New World Disorder*, *My West*, *Soft Touch (Acid House)*.

DAVID HARGREAVES
Man

RSC: *The Taming of the Shrew*, *King Lear*, *Romeo and Juliet* (all Stratford and London), *The Pilate Workshop*, *The Wars of the Roses* (Peter Hall and John Barton).
theatre includes: *Mr Puntila and His Man, Matti*, *The Hypochondriac* (Belgrade); *The Worcester Pilgrim* (Worcester Cathedral); *On the Shore of the Wide World* (Royal Exchange/National Theatre. Nominated Manchester Evening News Best Supporting Actor); *Mother Courage*, *Much Ado About Nothing*, *Othello*, *Rosencrantz and Guildenstern are Dead*, *Love for Love* (National Theatre); *Hamlet* (Birmingham Rep/tour/Elsinore); *Twelfth Night* (Birmingham Rep/tour); *Quarantine*, *All That Trouble*, *The Four Alice Bakers*, *Season's Greetings* (Birmingham Rep); *Kafka's Dick* (Nottingham Playhouse); *Lavochkin 5* (Tron, Glasgow); *The Changing Room* (Royal Court at Duke of York's/tour); *Antony and Cleopatra* (Riverside Studios/world tour); *A Passionate Woman* (West Yorkshire Playhouse).
television includes: *Casualty*, *The Bill*, *Heartbeat*, *Mersey Beat*, *The Passion*, *Making Out*, *Peak Practice*, *Bloomin' Marvellous*, *Bugs*, *Pie in the Sky*, *Beck*, *Expert Witness*, *Some Kind of Life*, *Hetty Wainthropp Investigates*, *Earthfasts*, *Ruth Rendell: Vanity Dies Hard*, *Harry*, *Justice for Gemma*, *The Tempest*, *The Mendip Mystery*, *Inspector Alleyn: Death at the Bar*, *The Miner's Strike*, *Madly in Love*, *Poirot*, *All Creatures Great and Small*.
film includes: *She's Been Away*, *Agatha*, *Othello*.

GILES CADLE
Designer
RSC: *The Tempest, A Midsummer Night's Dream.*

theatre includes: *No Man's Land* (Gate, Dublin/West End); *His Dark Materials, Southwark Fayre* (National Theatre); *Beckett Festival: 16 Short Beckett Plays* (New York/Barbican Centre); *Tom and Viv, The Shape of Things, The Hypochondriac* (Almeida); *A Prayer for My Daughter, Six Characters in Search of an Author* (Young Vic); *Festen* (Gate, Dublin).

opera includes: *Punch and Judy* (ENO at Young Vic); *Rusalka* (Royal Danish Opera); *Dido and Aeneas/Les Noces, Eugene Onegin* (Opera North); *Force of Destiny* (Israeli Opera/ Lithuanian Opera); *Lulu, The Midsummer Marriage* (Bayerische Staatsoper, Munich); *Boris Godunov* (New Zealand Opera); *The Barber of Seville* (Komische Oper, Berlin); *The Flying Dutchman* (New York City Opera); *The Beggar's Opera* (Opera du Rhin, Strasbourg); *The Magic Flute* (English Touring Opera); *Flight* by Jonathan Dove (Glyndebourne); *Katya Kabanova* (New Zealand Festival Opera).

Giles is designing future projects for the Geneva Grand Theatre and the Royal Opera House.

MARINA CARR
Writer
This is Marina's first time working with the RSC.

previous work in London includes: *Woman and Scarecrow* with Fiona Shaw, *On Raftery's Hill, Portia Coughlan* (Royal Court); *By the Bog of Cats* with Holly Hunter (Wyndham's).

other work includes: *The Mai, Ariel, Low in the Dark, Ullaloo, Meat and Salt. Marble*, her next play, will be performed at the Abbey Theatre, Dublin, in February 2009, as will a new children's play, *The Giant Blue Hand*, at The Ark, a children's cultural centre in Dublin. She is currently working on plays for the McCarter Theatre, Princeton, the Abbey Theatre and the National Theatre.

awards include: The Susan Smith Blackburn Prize, The Macaulay Fellowship, The E.M. Forster Award from the American Academy of Arts and Letters.

Marina has been a writer-in-residence at the Abbey Theatre and she has held the Heimbold Chair of Irish Studies at Villanova. She is the 1932 Fellow at Princeton University for 2008 and she currently teaches playwriting at Trinity College, Dublin, where she is Honorary Professor at the Samuel Beckett Centre for the Arts. She is a member of Aosdána, an Irish government body which gives a lifetime stipend to artists.

Marina lives in Kerry with her husband and four children.

SELINA CARTMELL
Director
trained: Central School of Speech and Drama, Trinity College, Dublin and Glasgow University.

theatre includes: *Big Love, Woman and Scarecrow* (Abbey, Dublin); *Sweeney Todd* (Gate, Dublin. Irish Times Theatre Award for Best Opera Production); *Festen, Catastrophe* (Gate/Barbican); *Here Lies* (Galway Arts Festival, Dublin/Paris); *Passades* (Operating

Theatre); *Sunlight at Midnight* (BAC); *The Nightingale* (Project). Selina is Artistic Director of Siren Productions. Productions for Siren include: *Macbeth*, *Titus Andronicus* (four Irish Times Theatre Awards including Best Production and Best Director), *La Musica* (Dublin Fringe Festival Best Production and Best Actress), *Fando & Lis*, *Shutter*.

Selina was a finalist in the Opera Europa/Camerata Nouva Europaische Opernregie-Preis (International Directors Opera Award, Wiesbaden, Germany, 2005). In 2006 she was chosen as a Protégé in the third cycle of the Rolex Mentor and Protégé Arts Initiative. Selina has just finished collaborating with her mentor, world-renowned director and designer Julie Taymor.

CONOR LINEHAN
Music

RSC: *The Taming of the Shrew*, *Macbeth*, *The Two Gentlemen of Verona*, *Edward III*, *Loveplay*, *Luminosity*.

other theatre includes: Conor has composed scores for theatre, dance and film throughout Ireland and Britain. *Little Wolf's Book of Badness* (Hampstead); *Intemperance* (Liverpool Everyman); *The Crucible*, *The Misanthrope* (Theatr Genedlaethol Cymru); *Peer Gynt*, *The Playboy of the Western World* (National Theatre); *The Wake*, *Saint Joan*, *The Colleen Bawn*, *Love in the Title*, *The Tempest*, *She Stoops to Conquer*, *The Cherry Orchard*, *Homeland*, *The School for Scandal* (Abbey Theatre, Dublin); *American Buffalo*, *A View from the Bridge*, *Long Day's Journey Into Night* (Gate, Dublin); *Dublin by Lamplight*, *Everyday* (Corn Exchange); *Antigone*, *The Crock of Gold* (Storytellers); *Mermaids* (Coisceim Dance Theatre); *Rebecca* (David Pugh Ltd.); *Rosencrantz and Guildenstern are Dead*, *Four Knights at Knaresborough* (West Yorkshire Playhouse); *The Mayor of Zalamea*, *The Mollusc* (Liverpool Playhouse and Everyman); *Carthaginians*, *A Doll's House* (Lyric, Belfast); *Twelfth Night* (Thelma Holt Productions). In addition he works extensively as a concert pianist. He has written the music for *The King with Horse's Ears* with the RTE Concert Orchestra for RTE Radio 1 and has written a piano concerto for the RIAM Big Band and Therese Fahy.

ANNA MORRISSEY
Movement Director

RSC: *I'll be the Devil* (RSC/Tricycle), *Timon of Athens* (RSC/Cardboard Citizens).
theatre and opera include: *Hansel and Gretel* (Opera North); *Hanover Square* (Finborough); *101 Dalmatians* (Theatre Royal, Northampton); *The Barber of Seville*, *Manon Lescaut* (Opera Holland Park); *Dr Faustus* (Resolution! The Place); *The Tempest*, *A Warwickshire Testimony*, *As You Like It*, *Macbeth* (Bridge House); *The Taming of the Shrew* (Creation Theatre Co.); *Richard III* (Cambridge Arts); *Hamlet* (Cliffords Tower, York); *The Arab-Israeli Cookbook* (Tricycle); *Human Rites* (Southwark Playhouse); *Julius Caesar* (Menier Chocolate Factory); *Tamburlaine the Great* (Rose).

Anna has worked as a practitioner within the RSC movement department and taught at E15, Queen Mary and Westfield and Shakespeare's Globe Education.

FERGUS O'HARE
Sound Designer
RSC: *I'll be the Devil* (RSC/Tricycle), *King Lear*, *The Seagull* (both Stratford/world tour/New London); *Volpone*, *Hecuba*.

other theatre includes: *Overspill* (Soho); *In The Red and Brown Water* (Young Vic); *Riflemind*, *The New Statesman* (Trafalgar Studios); *Rain Man*, *Fool For Love* (Apollo); *Translations*, *The Merchant of Venice*, *Guiding Star*, *Money*, *Noises Off* (National Theatre); *The Entertainer*, *The Tempest*, *Hamlet*, *Richard II*, *Cloaca*, *The Philadelphia Story*, *Aladdin*, *24 Hour Plays* (Old Vic); over 25 productions for the Donmar including *Merrily We Roll Along*, *Playland*, *Passion Play* and *Caligula*; *Intemperance* (Liverpool Everyman); *Tartuffe*, *Our Country's Good* (Liverpool Playhouse); *Whipping It Up* (New Ambassadors); *Rabbit* (ORL/Trafalgar Studios/59e59); *Improbable Frequency* (Traverse); *See How They Run* (Duchess); *Who's Afraid of Virginia Woolf?*. Work in New York, Los Angeles and Sydney includes: *The Shape of Things*, *A Day in the Death of Joe Egg*, *Dance of Death*, *Noises Off*, *Electra* (Drama Desk Nominee) and *An Enemy of the People*.

ELOISE PROUSE
Music Director
trained: Chetham's School of Music, Manchester and the Royal College of Music, London.
work includes: Regular freelance player with the City of Birmingham Symphony Orchestra and other ensembles including English Symphony Orchestra, City of London Chamber Orchestra, London Concert Orchestra, National Symphony Orchestra, Bert Kaempfert Orchestra, English Sinfonia and the London Concertante. Principal 2nd violin with the Guildford Philharmonic, London Soloists Chamber Orchestra and City Chamber Ensemble. She has also performed with the Carl Rosa Opera Company's West End season, *ABBA: the Show* (UK tour), Karl Jenkins and Symphonic Queen. Recently she has become more involved in popular music and has performed with such artists as Kanye West, Mary J Blige, Gnarls Barkley, Alison Moyet, Andrea Bocelli, Katherine Jenkins, David Garrett and Il Divo.
television includes: *GMTV*, Concert for Diana, *The Friday Night Project*, *This Morning*, *Top of the Pops*, *Parkinson*, *The Two Ronnies*, The Brit Awards.

MATTHEW RICHARDSON
Lighting Designer
RSC: *A Midsummer Night's Dream*, *Hamlet*, *The Park*.
theatre designs include: *Six Characters Looking for an Author*, *Doctor Faustus* (Young Vic); *The Birthday Party*, *Nine Plays and a Recipe* (Citizens Theatre, Glasgow).
opera designs include *Otello*, *Macbeth* (La Scala, Milan); *Eugene Onegin*, *Lulu*, *Pelléas et Mélisande* (Glyndebourne); *Fidelio*, *From the House of the Dead* (ENO); *Cherubin*, *Falstaff* (Royal Opera House); *A Midsummer Night's Dream*, *Moses and Aron* (Metropolitan Opera, New York); *Don Carlos*, *Julietta*, *Peter Grimes* (Paris Opera); *Les Troyens* (Munich Opera); *Jenufa*, *Mefistofele* (Netherlands Opera).
work as a director includes: *Macbeth* (Malmö Opera); *Rigoletto*, *Boris Godunov* (New Zealand Opera); *The Cunning Little Vixen*, *Turandot* (Norrlands Opera, Sweden); *The Marriage of Figaro* (BBC 2).

For the RSC at Wilton's Music Hall

Casting Assistant
JIM ARNOLD

Wardrobe Mistress
VALERIE ATKINSON

London Manager
CORINNE BEAVER

Head of Marketing
LYDIA CASSIDY

London Technical Manager
JULIAN CREE

Literary Manager
PIPPA ELLIS

Lighting Technician
MICHELLE ETHERINGTON

Head of Press
PHILIPPA HARLAND

Director of Sales and Marketing
CHRIS HILL

Producer
TARA HULL

Head of Casting
HANNAH MILLER

Company Dramaturg
JEANIE O'HARE

Casting Director
HELENA PALMER

Wigs Mistress
LOUISE RICCI

London Administration Assistant
LAUREN RUBERY

Wigs Swing
JENNIFER SIMONS

Assistant Casting Director
JANINE SNAPE

Senior Stage Technician
KATE STOKES

Senior Lighting Technician
ANDREW TAYLOR

Literary Assistant
DAN USZTAN

Stage Technician
ROBERT WEATHERHEAD

Senior Sound Technician
SARAH WELTMAN

Marketing, Sales and Advertising
AKA MARKETING
(020 7836 4747)

SUPPORT THE RSC

As a registered charity the Royal Shakespeare Company relies on public support and generosity.

There are many ways you can help the RSC including joining Shakespeare's Circle, RSC Patrons, through corporate support or by leaving a bequest.

RSC PATRONS AND SHAKESPEARE'S CIRCLE

By supporting the RSC through Shakespeare's Circle and RSC Patrons you can help us to create outstanding theatre and give as many people as possible a richer and fuller understanding of Shakespeare and theatre practice. In return you receive benefits including priority booking and invitations to exclusive supporters' events. Shakespeare's Circle membership starts at £8.50 per month.

HELP SECURE OUR FUTURE

Legacy gifts ensure that the RSC can develop and flourish in the years to come, bringing the pleasure of theatre to future generations that you yourself have enjoyed.

CORPORATE PARTNERSHIPS

The RSC has a national and internationally recognised brand, whilst retaining its unique positioning as a Warwickshire-based organisation. It tours more than any other UK-based arts organisation and has annual residencies in London and Newcastle upon Tyne. As such it is uniquely placed to offer corporate partnership benefits across the globe.

The Company's experienced Corporate Development team can create bespoke packages around their extensive range of classical and new work productions, education programmes and online activity. These are designed to fulfil business objectives such as building client relationships, encouraging staff retention and accessing specific segments of the RSC's audience. A prestigious programme of corporate hospitality and membership packages are also available.

For more information, please telephone **01789 403470**.

For detailed information about opportunities to support the work of the RSC, visit
www.rsc.org.uk/support

The Royal Shakespeare Company

Marina Carr
The Cordelia Dream

faber and faber

First published in 2008
by Faber and Faber Limited
3 Queen Square, London WC1N 3AU

Typeset by Country Setting, Kingsdown, Kent CT14 8ES
Printed in England by CPI Bookmarque Ltd, Croydon, Surrey

The right of Marina Carr to be identified as author
of this work has been asserted in accordance with Section 77
of the Copyright, Designs and Patents Act 1988

A CIP record for this book
is available from the British Library

ISBN 978-0-571-24262-7

2 4 6 8 10 9 7 5 3 1

For Dermot, William, Daniel, Rosa, Juliette

Characters

An Old Man

A Woman

Setting

A space with a piano

Time

The present

Act One

The Old Man sits at the grand piano playing a beautiful melody.
   The buzzer goes.
   He stops playing.
   He sits quietly, hands raised.
   He resumes playing.
   The buzzer goes again.
   He stops again.
   He resumes again.
   The buzzer goes again.
   The Old Man goes to the door.
   Opens it.

Man You.

Woman Yes. Me.

Man Well.

Woman It wasn't easy . . . seeking you out.

Man Wasn't it?

Woman I stayed away as long as I could.

Man You think I'm going to die soon?

Woman Maybe.

Man You want to kiss and make up before that event?

Woman Some people visit each other all the time.

Man I'm not some people. You of all people should know that.

Woman Can I come in or not?

Man stands back for Woman to enter.

Thank you. This is where you live now?

Man Yes.

Woman No trees. No grass. No birds. No sea.

Man Old men don't need scenery.

Woman What do they need?

Man Just a piano and a stool, a few pens, paper.

Woman Where do you sleep, eat?

Man I manage. Sit down.

Woman Where?

Man Here. (*Piano stool.*) Or there's the floor, the window. Let me take your coat.

Woman (*takes off her coat, hands it to him*) I brought wine, cheese.

Man I've no bottle-opener.

Woman I brought that too.

Man I don't drink now.

Woman You don't drink?

Man Not since my false teeth fell into the toilet. I drink water obviously and one cup of black coffee every morning.

Woman (*looking around*) Coffee. Where do you get that?

Man From women mostly.

Woman Women. Not one woman but women.

Man Does that annoy you?

Woman Yes, it does.

Man You want to be my coffee maker?

Woman One time I was.

Man I get coffee as a reward. Black. Steaming. I gulp it down. Scald on the throat, then a mad dash for the door before I'm asked to fix the washing machine or worse, speak the language of love and loss in the morning.

Woman What's wrong with the language of love and loss in the morning?

Man Love needs a streak of darkness. The day is for solitude. Morning especially. Morning is for death.

Woman And afternoons?

Man At your age they're for transgressions, at mine they're for remorse.

Woman You know about remorse?

Man I'm an expert on it. That's why I don't have an armchair. If I had an armchair I would sink into it and never get out of it again. Remorse is fine in its place. Whatever feeds the flame, as they say. And then there's the night, the arms of women.

Woman I wish you'd stop talking about them in the plural.

Man Women? Women are plural.

Woman And men?

Man We don't exist. We have pianos and stools. We part with semen to procreate. We are remorseful in the afternoon. At night we disappear into women. If we're lucky. That's men for you. Sometimes we read a book or two and have really strong opinions. We make grand statements on art, music, poetry, the state of the country, you name it, we can pronounce on anything. And what never ceases to amaze me is, people believe us – worse, take us seriously. And somehow that's enough, that sustains us for eighty years.

Woman You're not fooled?

Man Will I open that wine for you or are you just going to look at it?

Woman Only if you have a glass.

Man I couldn't. But I could drink water out of a wine glass if that helps.

Woman That would help.

Man I don't know why women are so afraid of drinking alone. When I was drinking I enjoyed others' company, but it was nothing to the marvels of myself I unlocked when drinking alone.

Woman Yeah.

Man You're not going to ask me what marvels?

Woman You're going to tell me anyway.

Man I discovered one thing. My soul –

Woman You're not the first to uncover his soul in his cups.

Man Let me finish. I discovered my soul stands appalled.

Woman Appalled. Why?

Man Appalled that it is attached to me. Trapped in time, stitched to me.

Woman Isn't every soul appalled with its mortal frame?

Man Some souls are smug. They can't believe their luck. Some fall in love with the earth. Imagine that.

Woman I have known moments when I'm in love with the earth.

Man You in love is one thing. Your soul is another. Your soul to be seduced by all of this. It's pathetic. Cars, houses, the rising sun, children romping in the garden come evening. To think it doesn't get better than this.

Woman I have five children now.

Man Yes, I heard you had another one.

Woman You're not curious?

Man About what?

Woman If it's a boy or a girl.

Man I'm not curious.

Woman If it's called after you?

Man That I think is unlikely.

Woman You're right there. It's not called after you. None of them are called after you. None of them ever will be.

Man Well, I'm glad we've sorted that out.

He hands her a glass, sniffs the bottle, pours.

Just as well I don't drink. I couldn't drink this.

Woman But it'll do for me.

Man You bought it. You decided you and I were not worth a good bottle of wine. No, we're worth an almost good bottle of wine. Though this wine is expensive, it's plonk. Let me give you some advice, my dear. Things are never what they seem. Never. Cheers.

Woman You're not going to congratulate me?

Man On what?

Woman On the new baby.

Man Why?

Woman It would be a normal response from someone in your position.

Man Congratulations.

Woman You take no joy in new life?

Man Why should I when mine is coming to a close?

Woman You're not sick, are you?

Man Why should I delight in birth after birth? What have your obsessions with maternity to do with me?

Woman Not even a card.

Man You don't want my cards!

Woman No, I don't.

Man My baby presents. I sent those baby things, those outfits to the others. What were they? Boys? Girls? I've forgotten. I sent or rather my women sent those baby rags. Did you reply?

Woman You really want me to reply?

Man Look, I've left you alone!

Woman Only after you lost. Only after there was nothing else you could do. You haven't left me alone. You've retreated to this sulphurous corner to gather venom for the next assault. You? Leave me alone? You haunt me.

Man I? Haunt you?

Woman I know what you're planning. I know it.

Man What am I planning?

Woman Your death. You're going to die and I'm going to be left with the fallout. I refuse to deal with your ghost. That's why I'm here. I want to sort you out while you're alive. While there's breath in my body.

Man Are you dying?

Woman Can I smoke?

Man Yes. Yes. Smoke. Smoke.

Woman What'll I use as an ashtray?

Man Flick it out the window.

He opens the window. White curtain blows in and out. Woman goes to the window. Stands there smoking. He looks at her.

You're very like her.

Woman Am I?

Man Standing there by the window, always at the window.

Woman I remember long ago when I loved you. A funeral and she was weeping, and I said, 'You look lovely,' and she did. I'd never seen her weep before. It suited her, tears suited her. For once she was open and real. And she caught me by the arm and hissed, growled, whatever that elemental throat sound is. 'Well, I feel far from lovely.' And suddenly you were there, between us, freeing my arm. 'Leave her,' you said, 'leave her alone, she's only trying to comfort you.'

Man Who would've thought I'd have it in me?

Woman To stand up for me?

Man To respond humanely. What did you have?

Woman What?

Man The baby?

Woman Another boy. I almost called him after you.

Man I understand.

Woman No, you don't.

Man Does he have long fingers?

Woman He does.

Man Musician's hands?

Woman Big and capable anyway for such a little fellow.

Man That's good. I hate small hands in a man, a boy, a male child. Women are so unwieldy. Without big hands they're impossible. And is your husband the father of all your children?

Woman What sort of a question is that?

Man Why not move around a little?

Woman There are things like fidelity. Stability. Love, even. I know they don't rate highly in your book but they exist nevertheless.

Man If I was a woman I'd have a different father for each child. Think of the variety, the expanding gene pool, the colour spectrum, from snow-white to blue-black. Really women are terribly conservative when it comes down to it.

Woman And who would feed this colour spectrum? Who would bind them together?

Man The world, of course. Don't tell me you've been seduced by the middle-class jaunt. The stable childhood, the good schools, the extracurricular activities. All death for the child. The only thing children need to learn is passion.

Woman They need to learn a lot of things.

Man No, only passion. Find the child's passion. Feed it. And you have an extraordinary individual. The rest are dodos. You see them up and down the streets of the cities and the kingdoms. The walking dead, and they're not seven. The walking dead nursing Mommy and Daddy's darkness.

Woman What about Mommy and Daddy's light? There's that too.

Man I've not come across it.

Woman You don't want to see it.

Man I'm telling you, just put them in a field. Leave them alone. That's my advice. Feed them, wash them occasionally. The rest will take care of itself. Only leave them alone. Leave them to their enchantments. They'll stumble across them if left alone. I did.

Woman Well, I didn't.

Man I don't know how you can say that in the light of what you have achieved.

Woman I have achieved nothing.

Man I know that. But the world thinks you have. There must be a golden shimmer off you. I could never see it.

Woman No, you couldn't.

Man The gods have favoured you.

Woman Is that what you think?

Man That is what I think and I ask myself why, because really, my dear, you are very mediocre.

Woman Does mediocre need 'very' in front of it?

Man When talking about you, yes, it does. A very mediocre gift I would say.

Woman I do the best with what I've been given.

Man And I don't?

Woman No, you don't. You haven't. It's too late now.

Man You're wrong, you know. Why do you think I've chained myself to this room, this piano? Why do you think I've given up kitchens and dining rooms and wine and champagne and cigars? I want the channels clear for all incoming signals.

Woman And are the signals incoming?

Man They're getting closer.

Woman This will be your great opus?

Man I'm listening. I'm waiting . . . Yes, it will.

Woman Not since Beethoven, they will say. Not since Mozart. Wagner. If you had the gift to match your ego.

Man I do, my dear, I do.

Woman Old men are always writing their magnificent opus. Their farewell to the earth. Their swan song. Most die in the middle of it.

Man At least I'll have attempted it.

Woman And I'm disturbing you. I'm botching the signals?

Man Yes, you are.

Woman I'll go so.

Man Finish your wine.

Woman Play me some of this magnificent swan song.

Man No.

Woman Why?

Man Because you'll steal it.

Woman I? Steal from you? You're too much.

Man You stole my gift!

Woman You had the field for fifty years before I came along. And what did you do in those fifty years? What did you do with that half-century?

Man I was limbering up. I was living.

Woman You were destroying all round you.

Man I was living. If I destroyed, then destruction is part of living. An artist will watch his mother die and wonder how he'll record it.

Woman Yes. Yes. Your poisoned anthem.

Man Isn't that why you're here? To record me. To put me into one of your mediocre compositions?

Woman Maybe. Yes. That's certainly part of it.

Man And the other part?

Woman I should've told you the minute I came in. It seems stupid now.

Man I contradict your idea of me?

Woman You talk too much.

Man Then let me listen a while to your pearls of wisdom.

Woman I came here because I had a dream.

Man You had a dream, so you came.

Woman That's all.

Man So what was the dream?

Woman About my life and my death. About your life and your death. We are horribly meshed. I dreamt of the four howls in *King Lear*.

Man When he carries the dead Cordelia on?

Woman Yes.

Man How is anyone meant to deliver those four howls? I've seen *Lear* more times than I can remember. Not one of them, and they were good, but not one of them could deliver those four howls to my satisfaction. It is four howls, isn't it?

Woman Yes. Four.

Man Not five?

Woman There's five nevers. Four howls. Some argue for three, that they're stolen from Hecuba.

Man The brazen genius of it. The four and the five. The proximity. It shouldn't work. It's wizardry. *Lear* is impossible.

Woman Yes, he is.

Man And his hanging daughter is risible. You think you're Cordelia to my Lear. No, my dear. You're more Regan and Goneril spun.

Woman And you're no Lear.

Man So that's what brought you here? A dream of Lear?

Woman A dream of Lear and Cordelia. Immediately you delete the woman.

Man So the woman is deleted. Can I tell you something about Cordelia?

Woman Please do.

Man Cordelia wanted to be hung.

Woman She did not.

Man Her death was necessary for her father's salvation.

Woman I won't be dying over you.

Man Won't you?

Woman You'll have to find your salvation elsewhere.

Man It was you sought me out. I've left you alone.

Woman You call writing to newspapers leaving me alone? Interviews! Photographs of you! Smiling! Your sordid jealousies spewed over my life, my children, my husband, my home! You call screaming at me in public leaving me alone! Your purple-faced obscenities, your paranoid speeches at my concerts, bullying and shrivelling me to a quaking ghost. You haven't left me alone! I've been hiding! You haven't been able to find me! Given one chance you'll annihilate me again. In the dream Lear comes on with the dead Cordelia and it's you and I. You have a cigar in your hand and a glass of champagne. You're wearing a tuxedo. I lie like a sack of drowned dogs at your feet and do you know what you say?

Man What do I say, Regan?

Woman You say, howl, howl, howl, howl, but it's the way you say it. Brazen. Cynical. Triumphant. And I'm dead. That'll be you at my funeral.

Man Perhaps it will. Perhaps it won't.

Woman All the clichés say hate is merely love twisted. I disagree. There is such a thing as pure hatred. Like you feel for me. It is very difficult to be so hated.

Man And what of your hatred for me?

Woman I am not capable of such hate. Such cold annihilation of the opponent.

Man You romanticise yourself.

Woman Do I? Women's hatred, at least mine, goes inward. It's directed at myself. Never underestimate how badly women feel about themselves. And how could we feel otherwise when you look around you? It's not a good time to be a woman right now. It hasn't been a good time to be a woman since the Bronze Age.

Man And that's my fault too?

Woman You take your superiority for granted. You think it is God-given. It isn't. This time will pass and with it all you dinosaurs. How dare you call me mediocre? You who haven't finished anything for years.

Man I am an old man who shouldn't have opened the door to you.

Woman Don't give me that helpless old man spiel. You're a vicious piece of work.

Man I don't want you dead. I just want you to go silent. Leave me the field for a while. I don't have much longer.

Woman You want me alive and silent? What is that but a sentimental form of murder? Why not have the courage to nail the lid on?

Man All I know is, for me to flourish you must be quiet. I would give anything for you to be quiet.

Woman People who know you, when you were part of the music scene –

Man I was never part of any scene, always the outsider. I never needed the herd like you and their ignorant approval. I was always beyond them.

Woman Well, I meet them from time to time, these people you were always above. They're still there, these elderly men valiantly working and finishing things despite their great age, and they always ask for you. Are you well? And are you proud of me? And for years I would smile and say yes, yes, of course he is. But recently I've stopped lying. It is very difficult to tell the truth. And when they ask now, I say, no, he's not proud. He's not one bit proud. And I watch the shock on their faces. It's a great conversation-stopper. I stand there with my cocktail sausage and my glass of Prosecco, I stand there and say, we're in competition. I say, the only thing that would make my father happy right now is to be putting flowers on my grave. At this point they excuse themselves and vanish into the crowd.

Man Because I put your mother into an early grave you think I'll do the same with you?

Woman Isn't that what you're trying to do? Isn't that where all your energies have gone this twenty years?

Man And what about your energies?

Woman All my energies go in staving you off. I have erected a force field around myself so you cannot get through.

Man But I do get through, my dear, don't I? I do get through.

Woman Three in the morning I wake from another nightmare of you, you're beating the door down, you come meaning harm. I get –

Man I am not responsible for your nightmares!

Woman I get up and wander the sleeping house. I check the doors, the children, fearful your black rays will invade their infant souls. The baby stirs. I hold his hand till he settles again. I go to the window, look out at the sea, light a cigarette. (*Whispers.*) My father, my father, I must cut him out of me. I must drain every last drop of his blood from mine. This silence of mine you crave. Well, you have it. I've done nothing for years.

Man You had two dreadful symphonies last spring.

Woman So you listened to them?

Man I listened! The better parts robbed from me! The weaker sections your own little attempt to strike out.

Woman They were made a long time ago.

Man And nothing since?

Woman A song cycle, a few sonatas, nothing to write home about.

Man It'll come back.

Woman I'm afraid it's gone.

Man And its going is connected with me?

Woman Have you listened to a word I said?

Man Now we're talking.

Woman This is not blame. This is beyond blame. This is tectonic plates, this is living, dying. This is cartilage, marrow, blood stuff.

Man Difficult to believe my blood runs through you. Difficult. And more difficult to accept this savage I see before me I had some part in making.

Woman You think I like looking in the mirror and seeing your tracks there?

Man If I could I would remove them. What star decreed we should be related?

Woman A malignant star from some awful furnace. One of us has to capitulate.

Man To go back to your Cordelia dream. When Cordelia dies, Lear does too.

Woman Meaning?

Man We won't survive each other.

Woman Don't say that.

Man But isn't it so?

Woman I know I'm more Regan and Goneril than Cordelia, but in the dream world, in the dream world we are shown our untrammelled selves before living mucks it all up. And you, though I would never equate you with Lear, for I have always loved Lear, I have to accept that somewhere buried inside you, deeply it must be, irretrievably buried, lies Lear, that arrogant foolish wise old man.

Man Your point?

Woman My point . . . I don't know what my point is. What the point of this black pilgrimage to your door is, except to tell you I had a dream about Lear and Cordelia. Just a dream, not even a recurring one, just one fleeting image of you and I and what we have come to. I wanted to tell you that. I probably shouldn't have bothered. And now I'll go.

Man But what is it you want?

Woman I want us both to live and flourish.

Man You want your gift back!

Woman Yes! Give it back!

Man You want me to come for Sunday lunch! You want me bridled! In awe of you? You want me to be proud of your petty achievements? You want me to marvel at my grandchildren? Grandchildren I have never seen!

Woman And whose fault is that?

Man Haven't you learnt anything? I am not the paternal kind.

Woman And why do you sound so proud, so wilfully proud that you are not the paternal kind?

Man I'm not. It's just a fact. The jaunt bores me. It bored me beyond belief with my own children. I'm not about to get into it again.

Woman There is no room for anyone in your world except you. And I don't think I could bear you at my table. No, I'm not talking about Sunday lunch or any of those common civilities that you despise. I'm talking about something different, older, something ancient, something civilisation is founded on.

Man And what is that, pray?

Woman The blood bond of parent and child.

Man You stopped being my daughter a long time ago.

Woman Yes, I stopped when I felt your claws around my throat, strangling all fledgling aspirations. Yes, I removed myself for protection, protection of this gift you spit on. I watched you. I gave you chances – too many! – to redeem yourself. I let you hold my firstborn. But I watched and I saw you wanted me to be a failure like you.

Man I am a great artist.

Woman I'm glad you think so, for no one else does.

Man I am a genius. A genius! And you are a charlatan! A charlatan who stole my gift when I wasn't looking. You are a charlatan who has plagiarised from everyone.

Woman That's what art is. Plagiarism and cunning disguise, a snapping up of unconsidered trifles. And coursing through it all, good faith, begging from above and underneath the throb of creation, that you are the first to do this, the last to do this, that you will surely die if you don't put something down. Right now! This minute! You think it's loose living, bad behaviour and the jottings of your hungover soul. It isn't. Artists are the most disciplined people on the planet. And I hope some day to call myself one.

Man That won't happen.

Woman No, not with you on my back it won't. Your pretensions are appalling. Your treatment of me is appalling. Of my mother, my siblings. Who gave you the licence to treat everyone so badly?

Man I am jealous of you.

Woman Jealous? Of me?

Man Yes. Jealous. It's hard not to be. You have a quarter of my gift, if even, but the gods have favoured you. They've put you on a list, some list I am excluded from. I walk down the street and they say your daughter this and your daughter that and how great it must be to have such a daughter and I say, yes, yes, it's great, great altogether, I pretend we are friends. Pretend I love you. Don't ask me why. It's not easy watch your own outstrip you. You wait, the clock moves, you wait till one of yours leaves you in the ha'penny place. And let me tell you something, I hope you never have the misfortune to have a child the likes of you.

Woman I think the only thing would make you happy is me removed from the Earth.

Man Yes. Yes. Remove yourself. Go. Do it now. Do it here if you wish. You vicious ingrate! When you were a newborn your mother and I couldn't bear to have you in the room. All the others slept in the cot beside us. You, we put away. Screaming the house down till we thought we'd go mad. We put you downstairs and let you scream. You'd scream for hours and one night I went down and stared at this screaming thing, blue with an untraceable rage, sweating and stinking. I tried to calm you. Nothing doing. I remember thinking I can do one of two things. I can pick her up or I can kill her.

Woman Hard to imagine you picking up a child.

Man Is it? Yes, I picked you up and walked you till you calmed and fell asleep. And that's as close as it gets to love, my dear. One night I refrained from smothering you in your blanket because you were small and pathetic. You're a bad egg. Well, there's one in every dozen.

Woman Yes, I'm a bad egg, but I was hatched in a dark place too.

Man You bet you were. All these unlovable children from that loveless bed. You're a horror, a nightmare. The old laws had it right. Foster them out. Let them like strangers be for strangers they are. Please go away. I have work to do.

Woman We can't part like this.

Man Oh yes, we can! You have come into my lair and savaged me again. You have come sauntering in with Lear on your lips and the pretence of reconciliation, when really you have come like the cuckoo to foul my nest, to clock and make sure I have not risen above the place you have allotted me. Well, you can see I have not, though I am trying.

Woman I wish you great success in your work. I know you don't believe that. But I do. I wish for them all to throw flowers at your feet. Maybe then you'll be happy. Maybe then you'll leave me alone.

Man No. I don't believe that.

Woman Well, believe it for this reason if no other. Every child wants a parent of note. I am no different. You flourishing would strengthen me. You articulating beautifully would give me great happiness.

Man Go! Go! Go! Before I hit you.

Woman You dare and I'll knock you to the ground.

Man Will you come to my funeral?

Woman Will you come to mine?

Man I'll be there.

Woman With your speech prepared.

Man With my speech prepared.

Woman So be it.

> *And exit Woman.*
> *Old Man stands there looking after her.*
> *Goes to window. Leans out.*
> *Hold.*
> *Music.*
> *Lights down.*

Act Two

Five years later.

The same room.

The Old Man reclines on divan, a cigar in his hand, ash wafting to the floor. A glass of champagne in the other hand. He conducts imaginary music. We hear it. Piano and strings. He allows music to wash over him. He is sublimely happy.

Enter Woman.

Woman The door was open.

Man Oh . . . hello, my dear.

Woman Do we kiss or what?

Man I'm always partial to kisses from women.

Woman kisses him.

Man Are you a nurse?

Woman You don't know me?

Man (*looks at her*) Give me time. Give me time . . . You're not my mother?

Woman No.

Man And you're certainly not a lover because all the women have disappeared, even Mozart's.

Woman Mozart's?

Man Did you know when Mozart died his widow sold his manuscripts? What was her name again?

Woman Constanza, wasn't it?

Man Constanza. That's the correct name for a composer's wife. But poor Constanza found it difficult to figure out how much her husband's manuscripts were actually worth. Then she had a brainwave. I'll sell them for the cost of the ink, she said. Don't you just love it? That's women for you. The cost of the ink. You're not the dog-hearted one are you?

Woman Who is the dog-hearted one?

Man The dog-hearted one that lives under the piano. You're not the vicious ingrate, are you? The vicious snake-eyed ingrate?

Woman I think maybe I am.

Man Then I'll get some twine and stitch your lips. I'll crucify your feet with wooden pegs. Oh my mother, my mother. Forgive me, my dear, all the long day I've been fighting off my mother.

Woman Have you?

Man She flies around the room on her broomstick, her grey hair spinning. She tries to haul me onto the broomstick and I spatter her to the wall. She's asleep now. Even witches have to sleep. Did you know that?

Woman I never thought about it.

Man Oh, they sleep in spite of themselves. They curl up on people's chests and sleep their malign suffocating snoozes. It's hard to breathe. Light my cigar, my dear.

Woman (*lighting it*) Don't you have an ashtray?

Man Champagne. Champagne. My glass is empty. She must have drunk it when I wasn't looking.

Woman (*pours for him*) Who brought you this?

Man One of my minions. He wants to be a great artist.

Like me. He wants all my secrets. I say, bring champagne and you shall have them. All my tricks, all my wizardry. He plays for me. Badly. I think he's a bit gone. I tell him, you have to be born with it. Born with it, do you see? You have to be disturbed, eternally dissatisfied, always watching, listening, waiting. I tried to explain this to him. He doesn't understand. He wasn't born with it. He believes in happiness. I say to him, good. It's a fine thing to believe in happiness, but you mustn't let it rule your life. We mustn't slide into happiness. The dog-hearted one also believes in happiness. She believes it is her God-given due. She believes I should adore her. And I do. Oh, how I love the dog-hearted one who has fouled my life.

Woman I heard your concerto for piano and strings.

Man And what did you think?

Woman A good first draft. A bit busy for me. It lacked beauty. You weren't in it.

Man Was I not?

Woman Why do you never finish anything?

Man A great artist never finishes a work, he merely abandons it.

Woman That's not true. Artists finish things. They finish things. Unless they die and maybe then they finish them properly in eternal time.

Man What would you know about eternity?

Woman You called it 'The Cordelia Dream'?

Man Yes. Why did I call it that?

Woman Yes, why did you?

Man I don't know where it came from. A snatch of something someone threw my way a long time ago. I wrote it when I was a young man before I knew anything.

Woman I was very proud to hear your name announced. Proud and moved.

Man Yes, it's nice to have one's name announced every now and then. As a child I loved gold stars, couldn't get enough of them from my teacher, used to buy packets of them in the shop and give myself gold star after gold star. Paste them on my legs. And what do you do if you're not a nurse?

Woman I don't do anything.

Man Then you're nothing.

Woman That's right. I'm nothing.

Man Do you even have children?

Woman Oh yes, there are children.

Man Well, that's something, isn't it? I had the most beautiful children once, sons, daughters romping in the garden. I forget how many, blond-haired, dark-haired, blue-eyed, brown, and some in between. The girls had long hair and giggled every time they saw me. Yes, I had beautiful children and then they were gone. What's the point of that?

Woman They don't come to see you?

Man They died. It was in the papers. They died eating cream buns, choked or something. Somebody said I did it.

Woman Well, one of them is here now.

Man Where? Oh, you mean the dog-hearted one, the vicious ingrate. Yes, she lives in the piano. Between her and the witch on the broomstick I have no peace. I even bought a gun and shot them. Still they whisper together in the dark. If you listen you'll hear them. Give me my hat.

She finds his hat, a woman's straw bonnet with flowers. He puts it on.

This hat frightens them. See. They're quiet now. They look at this hat with their mouths open. (*Opens his mouth.*) This was my wife's hat.

Woman I recognise it.

Man Throwing black shoes is no good. You need this hat and wooden pegs to crucify their feet. I have asked for wooden pegs. Repeatedly!

Woman I'm finding it difficult to get through.

Man To get through what?

Woman Oh . . . everything.

Man But that's the world, my dear. It is not easy for anyone. Anyone. Here, have a puff of my cigar.

    She has a puff.

Can I offer you some champagne?

Woman Is there another glass?

Man Have mine. Have mine. Don't upset me. I can't be upset. What's the matter? No tears. I can't bear women's tears.

    He takes out a handkerchief, dries her eyes.

No tears. Now, what is wrong?

Woman You'll go to your grave thinking I'm dog-hearted.

Man Are you?

Woman I never thought so, but you seem so certain.

Man No, I'm talking about one I brought forth. I'm not talking about you. You dog-hearted? You're a kind woman. I can tell. Look at me.

    They lock eyes. Hold.

(*Whispers.*) Oh my God. It's you. It's you.

Woman Yes. It's me.

Man The dog-hearted ingrate.

Woman I'm not.

Man Disguised as a woman.

He leaps up, runs behind the piano.

No. No. No. Keep away from me. Keep away. I thought I killed you.

He waves his hat.

My hat. My hat. Doesn't my hat frighten you?

Woman No, it doesn't.

Man (*runs to the window, shouts out*) Help! Help! Help! She's here. She came! She's here! Someone please help me. She's here with her army.

Woman Stop. Stop. Stop this.

Man (*terrified*) Now look what you've done. I've wet my trousers and my mother will go mad.

He looks up at the ceiling.

Now look what you made me do. Someone come and save me from this dog-hearted, snake-eyed, vicious ingrate.

Woman I just came to see you . . . I miss you.

Man Miss me. Well, miss me and be gone. Croak not, dark angel, I have no food for thee. The Prince of Darkness is a daughter.

He makes the sign of the cross with his arms to ward her off.

Woman Please, please, just listen for a minute. Give me one minute and then I'll go. I have left you alone for five years because you asked me to. I have stopped working because you asked me to. I have given you back your gift you said I stole. I have given you the field. Why have you not flourished?

Man Flourished?

Woman Yes, why have you not flourished? Why not one composition after another, one more beautiful than the next?

Man So I made something beautiful after all?

Woman No, you did not. Nothing beautiful. Nothing worth talking about.

Man Beauty takes time . . . it takes aeons and still there is no guarantee it will not all collapse down around your ears . . . My trousers are wet.

Woman Where do you keep your clothes?

Man My what?

Woman Your clothes?

Man My pyjamas are in the piano. Don't touch them! Don't you dare touch anything of mine.

He goes to the piano, opens it, takes out a pair of trousers, a pair of pyjamas, a toothbrush.

Keep off! Keep off, witch crab! Keep off.

He puts on pyjamas over his trousers, takes off his shirt, puts on the top of his pyjamas, brushes his teeth with toothbrush.

Woman Is it night?

Man When I put on my pyjamas it's night. Now where's the champagne? Devils should always be wrestled with champagne. The dog-hearted one doesn't like me drinking champagne. The dog-hearted one doesn't like me to enjoy myself. She would rather die than watch me swoon with pleasure. Well, look. (*Downs the glass.*) Now. What do you think of that? Where's my hat?

Woman On your head.

Man You are terrorising an old man. Who will forgive you for that? Who?

Woman I have no wish to terrorise you.

Man My wife and I had a goat-faced child. Goat-faced, dog-hearted with the soul of a snake. We buried her under the blue swing in the field of beech trees. But out she came, ate the coffin, clay in her eyes, and we took her in. My wife said, we'll pay for this. I said no, I had such faith in the heart of God. This is what she sounded like.

He plays a few notes on the piano.

And we loved this goat-faced, dog-hearted one as if she was our own. I even taught her the violin.

Woman Yes, you did.

Man I said, name your instrument as I said to all my children. Them all, she said for the dog-hearted one is insatiable. Them all. But being mediocre she settled for the violin, screeching 'Air on a G String' till we thought we'd go mad. My mother warned me about women like these. They come in on the night tide and bite the legs off lambs and suckle infant monsters, these mermadonnas with their thousand breasts and their slithering eel-like tails. Jewelled serpents with the appetites of wild dogs. And I promised Mother I would avoid such creatures and I did till I gave birth to you. They will carry you away, she said, away to their nightmare palaces of obsidian and painted coral, they will carry you away, and I fear you will.

35

Woman It seems I have already. Sit. Sit for a minute.

Man No, one can only kneel or stand in front of the dog-people. If I knelt would you forgive me my transgressions, though I don't know what they are?

Woman You know. Now sit. The dog-hearted one is asking you to sit.

Man Commanding me.

Woman OK, commanding you. Sit. Please . . .

Man If I sit will I be allowed up ever again?

Woman Of course.

Man Very well, I'll sit. See, I'm not trembling. This sweat is old age, not fear.

Woman Don't be afraid.

Man No, listen, what women don't understand is . . .

Woman What is it women don't understand?

Man What women don't know is all a man gets from the moment he's born is rejection.

Woman No, women don't understand that.

Man It's true. Forget the fat cats. Forget the unfeeling achievers. They're not men. I'm talking about the men who love music, who dream, who weep, they are lower than women.

Woman That low?

Man There is no place for them in this world. Anyone who would tolerate them is sick.

Woman I heard you had a great eightieth birthday party.

Man Did I?

Woman In Jimmy's house.

Man Jimmy?

Woman You gave a concert.

Man No, that was Schubert.

Woman It was you.

Man Me? No, no, no. I've finished nothing in twenty-five years. The dog-hearted one silenced me.

Woman No, you played, beautifully.

Man Did I? What did I play?

Woman You played me.

Man And who are you again?

Woman You couldn't be stopped. You had it all by heart. You knew all my scores.

Man One must always have the enemy by heart. You were there?

Woman No.

Man Why not?

Woman I wasn't invited. You couldn't be upset so I wasn't invited.

Man That's a pity. You're a good-looking woman. That's what concerts are for . . . good-looking women.

Woman And there was a party afterwards.

Man Was there? Why wasn't I asked? I love parties.

Woman The party was for you.

Man Really? You're being presumptuous.

Woman Jimmy comes to see you every day. He wants you to live with him.

Man No, my sons were drowned on a white ship, oh, a thousand years ago. All of them. And my daughters . . . To neglect an old man like this is inexcusable.

Woman They all still want you.

Man I know you do.

Woman No, I don't want you any more. I have no use for you now.

Man Because I'm old and weak?

Woman Because it's too late. The party, you enjoyed the party.

Man Well that's good. I enjoyed myself even if I don't remember. You were there watching me from outside the window. In the dark. I could feel you there.

Woman Seems I am always there.

Man You're mocking me. I haven't left this room since the dog-hearted one gave her express instructions for me not to move. Move left or right, buster, and I'll flay you alive like Marsyas was flayed by . . . by . . . what god was it flayed Marsyas? The one with the lyre and the garland in his hair. That's the one. You budge, mister, and that's what'll happen to you. I came up from the mountains of the south, at seventeen, to this city. My gift was prodigious. A genius, they said. I'd been schooled by an old fiddler back in the hills. He'd come into the kitchen every night and we'd play for hours. I learnt more from him than the so-called elite of this capital. Alcoholics. Mediocrities. All. They never heard dangerous music on the wind the way this old fiddler heard and caught it in his hand like he was cupping butterflies and gave it to me as if it were nothing. Scattering gold everywhere he went. I at least had the wit to stoop and collect. Is my hat there? (*Feels his head.*) I know you. You pretend you don't fear it, but

38

you do. You want me to take it off. Then you'll get me. Why aren't you snarling and baying for my blood?

Woman I'm taking a rest.

Man Oh, the dog-hearted one is tired. Do you want a bone? I have bones in the piano, elephant bones. Would you like a tusk to slobber on or is it me you're waiting for?

Woman It's you I'm waiting for.

Man How do the dog-hearted get through the day when they're not ransacking graves?

Woman With great difficulty.

Man Oh, they have their moments, have they? Their moments of remorse in armchairs?

Woman They certainly do.

Man And what have they to be remorseful for? I swear I've never seen a regretful wolf unless it's to regret there wasn't more in the carcass to devour.

Woman I regret my cruelty.

Man An apology?

Woman I regret my cruelty, but you were heartless too.

Man Never. Never. Never.

Woman You are wrong about me.

Man I am never wrong. That's what living intensely means. To be never wrong.

Woman I had to do what I did to protect myself.

Man Cordelia is blue when Lear carries her on. Blue from the neck up. Her tongue is four times its normal size. Her eyes bulge. I remembered all this when I wrote my Cordelia suite. Not a pretty sight. I said to myself, the colour of Cordelia is blue.

Woman And what colour is Lear?

Man Oh, Lear is the rainbow. He must go through all the colours till he is bleached to wizard. You know Lear's abiding feeling when he carries on the dead Cordelia?

Woman No, I don't.

Man Relief. Finally it's over. Lear is an old cynic. You can't teach Lear anything. Nothing moves Lear except Lear.

Woman That's nonsense. Lear changes and grows till the last second. Something you refused to do. Something I no longer have the courage for.

Man No, you just don't have it, do you?

Woman And you do?

Man You still dispute this?

Woman I don't dispute you were given something. What I dispute is what you have done with it.

Man Every time I turn on the radio they're playing you. You know why?

Woman Because I'm good?

Man Because you're easy, because you have a facility for jingles I could write in my sleep and often do and toss in the bin first thing in the morning. I have more pride. I am a great composer, yes, I am complex, erudite, difficult. I set trends. I am the winged horse to your braying mule.

Woman Your self-delusion is complete.

Man You have hounded me down the days of my life, down this one and down others I cannot clearly recall.

Woman Yes, it's bigger, isn't it? This battle between us? Ancient. Eternal.

Man You want my adoration?

Woman Once I did.

Man Men should not have daughters.

Woman When I meet my siblings we do not speak about you. Or rather I do not speak about you. That's the unspoken agreement, the condition of their company. I am only permitted to listen. I am permitted to hear first-hand, second-hand, third-hand how I have destroyed you. They quote your blubbering tirades. I don't always play by the rules. Sometimes I erupt, once I even dared to say the destruction is both ways. A shocking concept, you for once not genius martyr with a monstrous offspring but ordinary, flawed man. And another time I hissed what has destroyed you is that I do what you do only better. Marginally. I'm not proud any more but I think it is fair to say I do it better. Of course that cannot be acknowledged, not to mind spoken of. They lie across your altar like dead flowers, my siblings, you have cut them down. My playmates of long ago.

Man And have I cut you down? The tallest flower in the field?

Woman What do you think?

Man I think it is hard to believe you have siblings. I dread the thought of seeing them.

Woman You see them every other day. They're the ones bring you champagne and stack your ironed clothes in the piano.

Man And do they look like you?

Woman I'd say they look kinder, more dutiful.

Man Who cares about dutiful?

Woman You do, obviously.

Man They want me to die in an orderly fashion.

Woman Well, the country is full of orderly deaths.

Man The old man from back in the hills. The fiddler. My first and best teacher. Did you ever meet him?

Woman No.

Man No, of course he wouldn't have any time for you. He'd have banished you with some fairy tune he heard on the cliff. I went to his funeral. To his wake. He lay like a little hen. They'd decorated him with leaves and twigs. He looked like a new-hatched wren, lashless eyes staring out from this nest. His children were all mad. On the wall over this nest his fiddle hung, and when I entered the room to pay my respects the fiddle exploded. I have wondered since was that a good or a bad omen?

Woman An omen, to be sure.

Man I gathered up the pieces and I asked his demented children could I have them, the remains of his fiddle, could I buy it? No. It was going into the grave with him. Was that an orderly death?

Woman I would say that's the death of an artist. They die differently. Reminds me of Shelley. You know how they identified the drowned Shelley? He'd been in the water a couple of weeks.

Man They identified the drowned Shelley by a volume of Keats' poems which was found in his breast pocket, with the spine bent back. He must have been reading Keats when the squall came up. I think I've had this conversation before.

Woman Yes, you have.

Man With you?

Woman It was the first beautiful thing you ever told me.

Man And the second?

Woman You told me what a phoenix was.

Man The third?

Woman There was no third. You saw my hunger so you locked those beautiful morsels away from me. You locked your library away. You locked your piano.

Man I locked the piano for sure.

Woman From my mother.

Man Absolutely.

Woman She was good.

Man She wasn't bad.

Woman As good as you.

Man Don't be ridiculous. Far too heavy-handed. Her fingers were too short. Her ear was scattered. Too many things whirling in her to hear or be heard.

Woman Still, to lock the piano.

Man Couldn't she buy her own?

Woman She loved you.

Man I know. I took advantage. There can only be one winner in that situation. I was determined it would be me . . . and yet . . .

Woman And yet?

Man She took me too seriously. Look. I try very hard not to see people, see women as meat on legs. I try very hard.

Woman And do you see yourself that way?

Man What way?

Woman Meat on legs?

Man How dare you! How dare you! I was flung to earth with my gift perfected.

Woman And how were the rest of us flung?

Man My gift perfected! Not many are. Most come with half a gift, or a longing for the gift, or a smidgeen of a longing. I came with the gold. All I had to do was scatter it.

Woman Then why didn't you?

Man Did I not?

Woman You locked it up with the piano for fear anyone would get their hands on it.

Man Was that what I did? Then that was a mistake.

Woman Yes, it was.

Man Is that why you're here? To tell me my mistakes?

Woman I'm here because you are my father and you're going to die soon.

Man You want a clear conscience?

Woman Too late for that.

Man Decades too late, I would think. Have I succeeded in putting a curse on you?

Woman You have succeeded.

Man I've stopped you working.

Woman You have.

Man I've managed to do that?

Woman For ever.

Man For ever. That's an achievement.

Woman It makes you happy?

Man No, it doesn't make me happy.

Woman I don't believe you.

Man I am always humble in victory. I will try not to appear ecstatic.

Woman You have silenced me.

Man I have found the dog-hearted one's Achilles heel. I can take off my hat now.

Woman Yes, you can.

He takes off his hat.

Man Do you mind if I celebrate with a new cigar and a glass of the good champagne? This (*glass*) is everyday stuff.

Woman Celebrate away.

Man goes to piano, takes out a dusty bottle of champagne. Blows on it.

Man I've been saving this up for an occasion.

Woman And this is it?

Man This is it, baby. This is it. Your silence, my garrulity. I have the field again, my gift soaring, you a fledgling in the ditch. Will you join me?

Woman Drink to my own demise? Why not?

Man opens champagne.

Man There are two glasses in that box. Could you get them for me, please?

Woman does so, dusts them off, holds them out for champagne.

I thought you looked a little woebegone when you came in. I never dreamt of this. Are you sure I can dispense with the hat?

Woman Make up your own mind.

Man I have on a wooden cross under my pyjamas, so don't get any ideas.

Woman I have no ideas, no designs.

Man Good . . . good. (*Raises glass.*) To . . . to . . .

Woman To my death.

Man Yes.

They drink.

I'm curious. When did this silencing occur?

Woman Oh, it was gradual. It stole upon me so quietly, so softly, till one morning I woke and I knew the magic was gone, gone as quietly as it had come.

Man Yes, that's the way magic goes and comes, comes and goes. I'm glad you escaped with your life. I'm glad you're alive. You are my daughter, after all.

Woman Oh, but I'm not alive.

Man What are you saying?

Woman I thought you knew. I'm dead.

Man What?

Woman Didn't the siblings tell you? I imagine you were at my funeral.

Man I was at a gathering recently. Was that your funeral?

Woman It may have been.

Man There was lots of wine after and familiar faces and people kept shaking my hand. I thought I was at a concert. I think I may have made a speech. I'm sorry, I didn't realise it was you.

Woman That's all right.

Man Why do I suddenly feel afraid?

Woman Are you afraid?

Man (*puts on his hat*) Just a precaution.

Woman Don't you want to know how I died?

Man You hung yourself.

Woman How do you know that?

Man I'm guessing.

Woman An accurate guess.

Man Cordelia hung herself.

Woman Cordelia was hung.

Man Same thing. It was what I always wished for you.

Woman Death by hanging?

Man Just a fantasy. Not in my wildest dreams did I ever imagine.

Woman Is it hung or hanged?

Man I think the correct usage is hanged. You say I hung a picture. I hanged a daughter. Personally I prefer hung.

Woman So do I . . . And how will you die?

Man I will die bravely, smug as a bridegroom.

Woman Lear again.

Man But all those children? To leave them like that.

Woman To leave them like that. If the truth be told, we leave long before we depart. For a long time now I have been the ghost in that innocent group.

Man Well . . . my dear . . . well . . . always knew that savage note in you. Was there like a rope burn in all your music. The dominant note, I think it is reasonable to say now you've proved it.

Woman The rope note. No, I can't argue with that verdict now. You want to see the weals on my neck?

Man (*touches rope marks on her neck*) You always went too far, always had to go further than the next even if it meant taking yourself out. Your face is blue.

Woman Is it?

Man I was wondering why. You're too much, my dear. You're too much.

Woman Nine days ago.

Man Nine days ago? Let me check my diary. Nine days ago was when?

Woman The seventeenth.

Man The seventeenth . . . let me see . . . there's no mention of you dying here.

Woman No?

Man No. The seventeenth. Are you sure?

Woman Yes.

Man Why are you so sure?

Woman I chose that day. I like that number.

Man Well there's nothing. All I have for the seventeenth is . . . (*Reads.*) 'A cold bright winter's morning. I've spent the last hour looking out the window and thinking about act three of *Lear*. What a sublime act, act three is. When I was a boy the master used to stand me on the chair to declaim, yes, declaim *Lear*. My clothes were

48

always wrong, my feet were bare but up I would climb onto the table and declaim *Lear*. "Oh fool, I will go mad, let me not go mad." Or the great four howls at the end of act five or the five nevers. Those lines were written for me. I would howl and never with a passion I could not have possessed but somehow seemed to possess me, howling and nevering for what was, for what had never been and for what has yet to be . . .' That's all that's there for the seventeenth.

Woman Do you have an entry for the eighteenth?

Man Yes, I do.

Woman Read it.

Man Just a couple of lines.

Woman Read it for me . . . please.

Man (*reads*) 'It's late. I've just opened the champagne and lit a cigar. Spent the whole day sketching out "Lear's Lullaby". Had a bit of a breakthrough towards dusk. What can Lear sing about after Cordelia?' (*Pause.*) He can only follow her. Something momentous is about to happen.

Woman And has it?

Man Of course not. If you write something like that down it usually vanishes in the fog of wine and dawn. The gods hate pride and reserve their severest punishments for the proud.

Woman My passing doesn't merit an entry in your diary.

Man It seems not.

Woman Maybe they didn't tell you.

Man Did you enjoy your death?

Woman It was so-so. A bit quick.

Man That's all?

Woman No, that's not all. The youngest found me.

Man Found you?

Woman Yeah. Escaped from the housekeeper. They were meant to be on the beach. Rain . . . then home, I suppose. And he runs into my studio. I thought I'd locked the door, but there he was with his bucket and spade. Last image from this blue, blue globe, a child, my child, a bucket, a spade poised, small sand-covered toes.

Man Oh my dear. My dear. What can one say?

Woman I know. Forty-five thousand years will not wash that one clean.

Man And is it very different there?

Woman I'm still getting accustomed. It's strange, the colours, the light is different. The symmetry is dizzying. There's no champagne, though the air sometimes feels like a light golden wine, and the evenings are endless, and swarming, teeming, you can hardly move with the stream. But I'm heading up country soon, where they say it's quieter.

Man And do you miss the Earth?

Woman I miss it. I know how to live now.

Man I'd like you to leave.

Woman I'm here to give you a gift.

Man A gift?

Woman Yes. A parting gift. Sit at the piano. Please.

She takes his hand, leads him to the piano.

Man You won't harm me?

Woman Why would I harm you?

Man Because I have harmed you.

Woman If only you had admitted that when I was here.

Man It was too soon.

Woman And now?

Man Yes, too late.

Woman Come, sit and play for me.

Man Am I dying?

Woman Yes, you are.

Man You're going to take me out?

Woman It was you who said once that we won't survive each other.

Man That was just talk for dramatic effect.

Woman And this is real?

Man With you gone the space is immense. I feel I could do anything now.

Woman Come and play for me. I want to give you a few notes.

Man I don't want your notes. I have never needed your notes.

Woman You'd like to die at the piano, wouldn't you? Mid-composition?

Man I don't want to die at all.

Woman Suit yourself. But let me tell you something before I begin the long gallop ahead. I was the most beautiful thing in your life. I was. And you didn't know it.

Man I did and I didn't.

Woman No, you didn't know it. You wanted the most beautiful thing to be you. Even still you fight me, I who have come from beyond the grave to tell you otherwise. I am dust now and before this hour is over you will be dust too. Dust. The winds here won't even bother to blow us away.

Man That is your parting gift?

Woman I was hauled before them, and you know what they told me? That the way I have lived is unforgivable, and I reckon they will tell you the same. Be afraid, they are savage here. The indisputable savagery of the wise and the true.

She lays her hands on his hands.

This is my gift. Close your eyes and play. This is what eternity sounds like.

Man plays a beautiful, haunting sonata.
Lights fade.

End.